Explore the Jurassic Coast

'Look around and read great nature's open book'...

So reads an anonymous quotation carved into rock at Durlston in Dorset. There is simply no better way to read and absorb 'great nature's open book' than by exploring the Jurassic Coast.

The Jurassic Coast is a 95 mile stretch of coastline (between Exmouth in Devon and Old Harry Rocks in Dorset) which is so special and important to the Earth Sciences, it has been given World Heritage Site status by UNESCO. It is the only **natural** World Heritage Site in England – you will have heard of other World Heritage Sites in the UK such as Stonehenge or Hadrian's Wall, but these are cultural Sites. The Jurassic Coast was granted the international status because the rocks along the Site record 185 million years of the Earth's history...

Yes, that's 185 million years of Earth history in 95 miles (155 km) of coast. There is nowhere else in the whole world where you can, quite literally, take a 'walk through time', and explore the Triassic, Jurassic and Cretaceous periods of geology.

Your chance to win a Family Activities Holiday
In this guide are 12 questions about the Jurassic Coast. If you can answer 6 correctly, you could win a fun-packed activity holiday on the Jurassic Coast.

Prize to be won!

1

How do I enter the competition?

This is not an armchair Explorers Guide!

Answers on information panels

If you want a chance of winning a fun-packed family activities holiday, you need to get out and about along the Jurassic Coast and find the answers to the questions. Each answer can be found on the information panels located along the coast. We'll tell you exactly where the panels are but it's up to you to head down to the coast and find the answers to the questions. An activities holiday is up for grabs once a year for 3 years and you can enter in one of the following years:

1. 1st May 2005 until 1st Oct 2005
2. 1st Nov 2005 until 31st Oct 2006
3. 1st Nov 2006 until 31st Oct 2007

Don't worry if you don't get to all 12 locations. As long as you have 6 correct answers, you've got a chance of winning.

To enter, write your answers on the competition reply card on page 27 and return it to us at the address shown, or you can enter online at www.jurassiccoast.com and click on 'Explorers Competition'.

PANEL LOCATION!

IS STAMPED ON EACH PAGE.

GR: Grid reference

REMEMBER

Questions:
Are indicated on each page like this!

EAST DEVON

Beer

Jacobs Ladder
Sidmouth

Budleigh
Salterton

Orcombe
Point

Now for the serious bit... by completing your Explorers Guide, you are helping to look after this special place. Did you know that all the profits from this guide have gone into the conservation of the World Heritage Site? You can also be a big help to us while you're visiting the Jurassic Coast by telling us if any of the information panels need repairing. That way, we can mend them quickly so everyone who visits can always read about this exciting area. Please contact us –

jurassiccoast@dorsetcc.gov.uk or **01305 225101** – and thank you for helping to look after the Jurassic Coast.

www.jurassiccoast.com click on 'Explorers Competition'

DORSET

EAST DORSET

PURBECK

Old Harry Rocks

Durlston Head

Lulworth Cove

Chesil Beach

Portland Bill

mouth

Key | Triassic Rocks | Jurassic Rocks | Cretaceous Rocks

Visiting the coast

Exploring the Jurassic Coast is best done on foot or by sea. The **South West Coast Path National Trail** provides a continuous footpath hugging the entire length of the Jurassic Coast. You don't have to walk all 95 miles unless you want to though – it's easy to find and follow a short section anywhere along the coast. Just look for the signs marked with the National Trail acorn and the words 'Coast Path'.

Boat trips are available from various locations along the coast. It is an excellent way to see the World Heritage Site and most boat owners will explain the geology of the coast to you as you sail along. Boat trips are advertised around local harbours and Tourist Information Centres also have details.

The Jurassic Coast bus (CoastlinX 53) is another great way of exploring the Site. Make sure you get on the top deck of these bright and colourful double deckers to get the best views! The bus runs every two hours between Exeter and Poole with lots of stops on the way. You can hop on and hop off wherever you like and a day ticket costs just £5.

The National Trust owns and manages nearly a third of the land along the Jurassic Coast.

THE NATIONAL TRUST

How to get here

Please call Traveline on **0870 608 2 608** for specific public transport information.
('How to get here?' will also be on each page and generally refers to getting to the nearest village or town. You will need to walk to most of the panels to find the answers to the questions).

Areas of Outstanding Natural Beauty

Most of the Dorset and East Devon coast and countryside is an Area of Outstanding Natural Beauty which means the area is managed to conserve and enhance the landscape and the lives of the people who live there.

Safety first!

- Beware of cliff falls and mudslides – always stay away from the cliffs
- Check the tides and take care especially in rough weather
- Avoid excessive hammering and do not try to collect large fossils from the cliffs as this may cause damage
- Keep away from cliff edges and follow the country code

HAVE YOU MADE AN IMPORTANT FOSSIL FIND?
Tell us about it by contacting the nearest visitor centre or the World Heritage Team on
01305 225101

5

Orcombe Rocks

Orcombe Point, Exmouth

The start of the World Heritage Site marks the start of the Triassic period... Why are the cliffs here so red and just what did this landscape look like 250 million years ago?

We start exploring at the western end of the Jurassic Coast. Here you'll find the oldest rocks – in fact, they are an incredible 250 million years old! The rocks are from the Triassic period and geologists can tell from the distinctive red coloured cliffs that this area used to be desert-like, with sand dunes and salt lakes, similar to Namibia in Africa today.

Desert life

Geologists can tell that the Triassic deserts here in East Devon would have been crossed in places by fertile river valleys. In the sandstones and pebble beds, geologists have found ripple marks and channels, indicating that water must once have flowed through the area. The discovery of fossilised plant, insect, fish and reptile remains prove that these ancient river valleys would have been fertile enough to support such life.

In geology the present is always the key to the past – it's just a case of knowing where to look and what to look out for (but remember to leave any close investigation of cliffs to the experts, as there is active erosion along the whole Jurassic Coast).

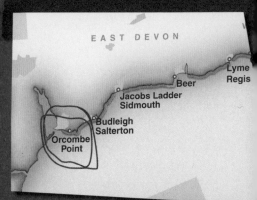

EAST DEVON

Lyme Regis
Beer
Jacobs Ladder
Sidmouth
Budleigh Salterton
Orcombe Point

The 'Geoneedle'

The pyramid like structure you see on top of the cliffs is called the 'Geoneedle'. It was unveiled by HRH The Prince of Wales in 2002 to celebrate the new World Heritage Site.

Did you know?

The Jurassic Coast reveals 185 million years of the Earth's history because earth movements caused the rocks to be 'tilted' from west to east. This means that the oldest rocks remained above sea level in the west, but dropped deep below sea level in the east. Younger rocks were then laid down on top and where erosion created today's landscape, we have been left with 250 million year old rocks in East Devon and 65 million year old rocks in Purbeck in Dorset!

PANEL LOCATION!
Take a short walk from the Queen's Drive esplanade, up the zig zag path and along the striking red cliffs owned by the National Trust.
GR: SY 021795

Question:
What causes the striking red colour of the cliffs?

7

Budleigh Salterton (Lime Kiln)

Budleigh Pebbles are possibly the most well travelled pebbles in Europe. They started life over 400 million years ago in what is now Brittany in France. 240 million years ago, during the Triassic, they were transported by vast rivers to the south coast of England and in Budleigh, they formed the Budleigh Salterton Pebble Beds. Today, longshore drift causes some pebbles to continue their journey as far east as Hastings in Kent.

What are the Budleigh Salterton Pebble Beds?

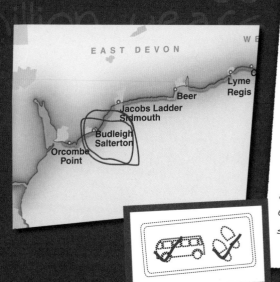

If you walk westwards from the Lime Kiln car park and look at the cliffs (don't get too close, as they are eroding), you will see pebbles which were transported by the ancient rivers during the Triassic and then 'sealed' in the cliffs, forming the Pebble Beds. You'll find plenty of Budleigh pebbles on the beach - they are often a perfect oval shape and are usually shades of pink or grey with a lovely smooth surface. They are also very durable which explains why they have survived 400 million years.

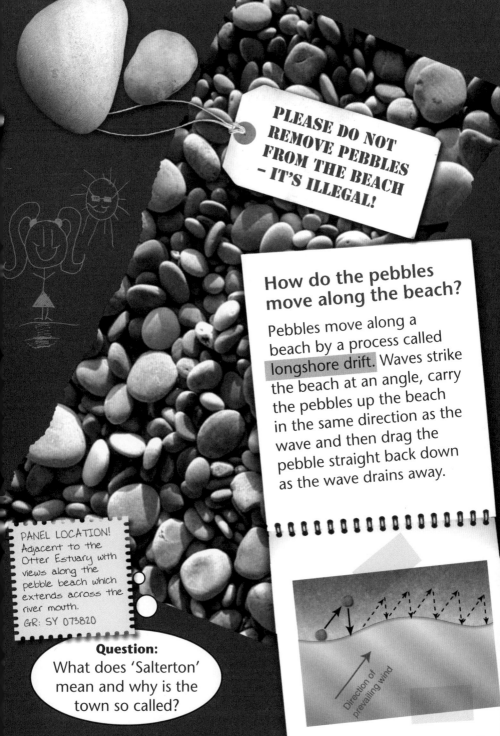

PLEASE DO NOT REMOVE PEBBLES FROM THE BEACH – IT'S ILLEGAL!

How do the pebbles move along the beach?

Pebbles move along a beach by a process called longshore drift. Waves strike the beach at an angle, carry the pebbles up the beach in the same direction as the wave and then drag the pebble straight back down as the wave drains away.

PANEL LOCATION! Adjacent to the Otter Estuary with views along the pebble beach which extends across the river mouth.
GR: SY 073820

Question:
What does 'Salterton' mean and why is the town so called?

Direction of prevailing wind

9

Jacob's Ladder, Sidmouth

The dawn of the dinosaurs

Within these red rocks, experts have found evidence of reptiles such as Rhynchosaurus as well as remains of amphibians and fish. Although the landscape was predominantly desert, there were wide shallow rivers supporting plants, insects and animals. It was during this time that the first dinosaurs evolved as well as the first true mammals.

The Otter Sandstone between Sidmouth and Budleigh Salterton is one of Britain's richest sources for mid-Triassic reptile remains and ranks as one of the most important places in the world to see these fossils.

Although Triassic fossils are rare and collecting must be left to the experts, fossil finds within these red rocks are very important and help us to reconstruct past environments from 230 million years ago.

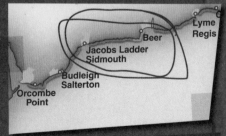

PANEL LOCATION!
Climb to the top of Jacob's Ladder and the panel is on the viewing platform overlooking the beach.

GR: SY 120869

Question:
What did the Rhynchosaur eat?

Beer stone has been used in 24 cathedrals, including Exeter and St Pauls, as well as parts of Westminster Abbey, the Tower of London, Hampton Court Palace and Windsor Castle.

Suddenly, the red rocks of East Devon change and younger white Chalk cliffs emerge around the pretty fishing village of Beer. In the midst of the coastline's oldest Triassic rocks, these much younger Cretaceous rocks seem out of place. What is going on?!

Well, the Cretaceous rocks are in fact 'out of place'! The Chalk rocks formed in a shallow sub-tropical sea about 70 million years ago and covered the whole area. Most of the Chalk was then eroded away but at Beer a fracture in the rocks has allowed the younger Chalk to drop to sea level.

Did you know?

This layer of Chalk continues behind the village of Beer where it forms a high quality masonry stone called Beer stone. The stone has been quarried since Roman times and today you can visit the underground quarries which cover an area equivalent to 50 football pitches. At Beer Quarry Caves fascinating guided tours bring to life the history of the local quarrying and the buildings it was used for.

As you explore the area, look out for the distinctive Beer stone used in the towns and villages of this part of the World Heritage Site.

The underground quarry was first worked by the Romans.

PANEL LOCATION!
As you descend to the beach, the panel is on the viewing platform to the right of the slip way.

GR: SY 230892

Question:
What are coccoliths?

Lyme Regis (Broad Ledge)

You have now entered the Jurassic period... when dinosaurs walked the earth and giant ichthyosaurs swam in warm shallow seas. Evidence of this remarkable past is all around you – you just need to know where to look!

Lyme Regis is a great place to explore. Head down to Monmouth Beach to see the 'ammonite graveyard', a ledge which is exposed at low tide and is crammed full of ammonites – but do make sure you are on the beach when the tide is going out. Stroll around and enjoy the town itself. A visit to the Philpot Museum is a must – the museum, Dinosaurland and fossil shops run guided walks with local experts which offer one of the best ways of familiarising yourself with the area.

Lyme Regis was the home of one of the world's greatest fossilists. Mary Anning (1799 – 1847) lived here all her life and discovered some of the most important fossils ever found anywhere. It was her extraordinary finds which led to the first ever reconstruction of a past environment by Sir Henry De La Beche in 1830. This drawing was the forerunner to the Jurassic Park movies!

Our very own unique dinosaur

Fossil collecting is still as popular today. Professional collectors have found some spectacular fossils. In 2000 a near complete skeleton of a dinosaur called Scelidosaurus, which is unique to Lyme Regis and Charmouth, was found.

Question:
What is the name of the most active coastal landslide in Britain?

PANEL LOCATION!
At the eastern end of Lyme Regis, walk to the end of the new sea wall where you will find the panel.

GR: SY 346923

12

How come we haven't 'run out' of fossils?

Sometimes people are surprised that there are still fossils left - after all, people have been collecting here for over 200 years! Well, the reason that we keep finding fossils along this part of the Jurassic Coast is because the cliffs are battered by storms and high tides and keep eroding, revealing new fossil finds.

WEST DORSET

DEVON

Charmouth
Lyme Regis
Beer
Jacobs Ladder
Sidmouth

HAVE YOU MADE AN IMPORTANT FOSSIL FIND?

Tell us about it by contacting the nearest visitor centre or the World Heritage Team on

01305 225101

Ammonites

Charmouth

One of the best places to look for fossils in the UK... you never know what you might find!

Everybody likes to go to the beach when it's hot and sunny, but if you want to try your hand at fossil collecting, the best time to go is after rough weather in the winter time. This is because storms, high seas and heavy rain do the hard work for you by washing the fossils onto the beach, where they then get washed clean by the sea. Don't look in the cliffs – not only are the fossils here soft and crumbly, but it can be very dangerous as rock falls are common.

Golden Cap from Charmouth

Charmouth Heritage Coast Centre

Located right on the sea front, the Centre is a great place to go to learn about the area and to get advice on fossil collecting techniques. The centre regularly runs guided walks and events – details can be found at the centre or click on

www.jurassiccoast.com or **www.charmouth.org**

Fossil Collecting Code of Conduct

The best place to find fossils is on the beach **NOT** in the cliffs... the soft mud and clay gets washed away from the fossils and leaves them spanking clean for you to find. It's much safer to collect on the beach, as the cliffs are constantly eroding and might fall on your head. Keep collecting to a minimum – leave some for others – and only collect loose fossils.

Never collect from walls or buildings – obviously! Please read notices and if they ask you not to collect, don't. These signs are there for a reason – usually your safety.

World famous fossils

The rocks around Charmouth are from the Jurassic era. They were laid down in a deep tropical sea 195 million years ago. The rocks here are bursting with fascinating fossils but remember to follow the Fossil Collecting Code of Conduct (a leaflet is available from visitor centres) and look for fossils on the beach. Remember too that the best tools to find fossils are sharp eyes. The remains of ichthyosaurs (large marine reptiles) are sometimes uncovered on Charmouth beach, although more common finds are ammonites and belemnites. People have collected fossils here for more than 200 years.

belemnites (relative of ammonites much like our modern day cuttlefish)

HAVE YOU MADE AN IMPORTANT FOSSIL FIND?
Tell us about it by contacting the nearest visitor centre or the World Heritage Team on
01305 225101

PANEL LOCATION!
Sea front
car park.
GR: SY 365930

Question:
What is the scientific name for a sea lily?
(It begins with 'C'!)

Chesil Beach and the Fleet is a SSSI - Site of Special Scientific Interest

PLEASE DO NOT REMOVE PEBBLES FROM THE BEACH IT'S ILLEGAL!

Nothing can prepare you for your first sight of 'the great beach'... a 17 mile (28 km) shingle bank which is one of the finest barrier beaches in the world. It has stood up to the full force of the Atlantic ocean for thousands of years and protects the Fleet, the largest tidal lagoon in Britain.

The Chesil Beach Centre at Ferrybridge should be your first port of call for finding out more about Chesil Beach and the Fleet.

How did the beach form?

Well, nobody really knows for sure! The most likely explanation is that rising sea levels following the last Ice Age about 7,000 years ago collected rock debris from landslides in West Dorset and East Devon and released it onto the shoreline. Longshore drift then carried the pebbles eastwards. The beach continues to move at a rate of about 15 millimetres a year.

Chesil Beach from Abbotsbury

When you explore Chesil Beach, you will notice that the pebbles in the west are so tiny that they are almost sand, yet the further east you travel, the larger they become. This pebble 'grading' is another unexplained phenomena surrounding the mysterious Chesil Beach... it may be because waves carry larger pebbles faster than smaller ones. Local folklore claims that smugglers landing on the beach in the dark of the night knew exactly which part of the beach they were on, just by feeling the size of the pebbles!

You are unlikely to encounter any smugglers here today, but it is important to be aware that the beach drops steeply into the sea and large unexpected waves can occur at any time. It is **UNSAFE** to swim here.

PLEASE DO NOT REMOVE PEBBLES FROM THE BEACH – IT'S ILLEGAL!

No Swimming

PANEL LOCATION!
Abbotsbury beach car park.

GR: SY 561848

Question:
About how many tonnes of pebbles make up Chesil Beach?

17

Portland Bill

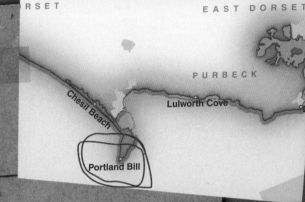

RSET   EAST DORSET

PURBECK

Chesil Beach

Lulworth Cove

Portland Bill

The Isle of Portland is a remote and spectacular place, extending five miles out to sea and regularly pounded by rough seas and huge tidal currents.

The whole of the island is a place to discover wildlife, birds, geology and the Portland heritage of building stone, or just to absorb the wild landscape and superb views.

Portland Stone is probably the most famous building stone in the world. The island is covered with quarries – Tout Quarry in particular is a great place to visit with an exciting sculpture trail to explore.

Worldwide links

The famous Portland stone has been used to build some of the world's most well known buildings. After the Great Fire of London in 1666, Christopher Wren chose Portland Stone to rebuild St Paul's Cathedral. It has actually been used in the building of seventeen cultural World Heritage Sites.

Portland Ribbon Wave

Won't we run out of stone?

Portland stone was first used by the Romans and continues to be used today. So how come we haven't 'run out'?

There is a finite amount of stone on the island... however, the whole island (which is four miles long and one and half miles wide (6.5km x 2.5km) is dominated by the hard Portland Stone. That's an awful lot of stone! New quarrying techniques include underground quarries which tunnel through rock layers without affecting what is above. Portland could become a maze of tunnels with huge pillars holding up the 'roof'. So, although we could indeed one day run out of Portland stone, it is unlikely to happen in the foreseeable future.

Did you know? The Isle of Portland isn't actually a true 'island' because Chesil Beach connects it to the mainland.

DINOSAUR FOOTPRINTS are sometimes uncovered in quarries on Portland

PANEL LOCATION!
Portland Bill
Lighthouse car park.

GR: SY 678684

Question:
What are the fractures called which criss-cross Portland Stone and help the quarry men work the stone?

19

Lulworth Cove and Stair Hole

Lulworth Cove is a perfect horseshoe-shaped bay created by the power of the sea. The narrow entrance is part of a band of hard, resistant limestone, whereas the rocks behind are much softer and therefore erode more quickly, allowing a beautiful wide bay to form.

If you walk a short way to the west of Lulworth Cove, you will come to Stair Hole where you can see another bay being formed through the collapsing of caves and arches. The impressive Lulworth Crumple on the eastern side of Stair Hole is a complex fold formed by dramatic earth movements – the same ones which created the Alps 35 million years ago.

Lulworth Heritage Centre is the place to go to learn more about this area. As well as excellent displays, the Centre regularly runs guided walks – check out www.jurassiccoast.com, 'What's On' page or www.lulworth.com for more information.

(For those who have difficulty using steps, cross the grass behind the coastguard cottages and walk east towards the sea. The panel will be on your left at the top of the steps behind the boat house.)

The Fossil Forest

To the east of Lulworth Cove lies the Fossil Forest. Instead of finding trees in this 'Jurassic Jungle', you'll see huge doughnut shaped algal burrs which fossilised around the base of the giant trees which grew here 140 million years ago.

The Fossil Forest lies within the 'range walks' which are part of a military firing range. The range walks are open most weekends of the year and during school holidays. Call 01929 462721 ext 4819 to check opening times.

Durdle Door

If Lulworth is the perfect bay then Durdle Door is the perfect coastal arch. Earth movements have tilted the rocks until they are almost vertical and the limestone barrier has since been virtually destroyed to leave this self-supporting natural landform. Durdle Door is half a mile west of the Cove.

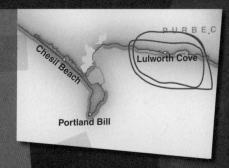

PURBEC
Chesil Beach
Lulworth Cove
Portland Bill

PANEL LOCATION!
Go down the road to Lulworth Cove and you will find a set of steps behind the boathouse on the right (as you face the sea). Go up the steps and the panel is situated at the top.

GR: SY 824799

Question:
How many types of rock can be found at Lulworth Cove?

Durlston

Durlston Head offers fine views of the English Channel and the Isle of Wight. The visitor centre and Country Park are excellent sources of information and run guided walks where you can learn more about the geology, birds, wildlife and art in the landscape which make this such a special area to explore.

Photograph by Roy Eggleston

EAST DORSET

PURBECK

Old Harry Rocks

Lulworth Cove

Durlston Head

LOOK AROUND AND READ GREAT NATURE'S OPEN BOOK.

PANEL LOCATION!
On the South West Coast Path, east of the Great Globe, facing north across Durlston Bay.

GR: SX 036772

22

PUFFINS

Bottlenose dolphins
Seabird colonies
kittiwakes
Peregrine falcons

Wildlife and birds

Bottlenose dolphins are regularly sighted from Durlston. Seabird colonies, including puffins and kittiwakes, and nesting peregrine falcons make the south-facing limestone cliffs along this stretch of coast their home.

Did you know?

Durlston Park was the creation of George Burt, a member of the family who started the Mowlem construction company. Burt's vision was to create an artistic landscape inspired by nature. His Great Globe (a 40 tonne sphere of Portland Stone), showing the world in 1887, is one of the most impressive features, but make sure you also read the evocative inscriptions carved into stone throughout the Park.

Durlston Castle was Burt's great folly and is now being developed into a visitor centre (due to open in 2008). A cafe serving locally sourced food is already open. Pop in for refreshments and enjoy near 360° views of the Jurassic Coast.

To Swanage

Steam train to Swanage.
(from Norden park and ride
via Corfe Castle).

Question:
What does the term 'discordant coastline' mean?

23

Old Harry Rocks

Here you are at the eastern extreme of the World Heritage Site where the youngest Cretaceous rocks dominate. The Site ends just beyond the Chalk headland of Ballard Down and the white Chalk sea stacks known as Old Harry Rocks. This beautiful area of Chalk downland and Studland Beach are managed by the National Trust.

 THE NATIONAL TRUST

How did Old Harry Rocks form?

Waves attacked the weak joints in the rocks to form arches and caves. These eventually collapsed, leaving isolated stacks like Old Harry. This is an ongoing process and until the 1890s, Old Harry had a 'wife' who collapsed into the sea!

You can usually see the Isle of Wight from this part of the Jurassic Coast. The Needles on the island are also made of Chalk and would have been joined to Ballard Down until the sea broke through just a few thousand years ago. In geological time, this is seen as 'recently'!

Formation Stacks

Stage 1
An arch forms in the Chalk as the sea works into weaknesses in the rock.

Stage 2
The arch gradually enlarges as more and more Chalk is eaten away.

Stage 3
The arch eventually collapses into the sea, leaving the seaward pillar as an isolated stack.

What is Chalk?

Chalk is a white limestone, formed in vast warm seas surrounded by deserts about 100 to 65 million years ago. It is composed of billions of microfossils.

The Chalk downland is home to many wild flowers and grasses which attract rare and unusual insects, including Chalkhill Blue and Adonis Blue butterflies.

Chalkhill Blue Butterfly

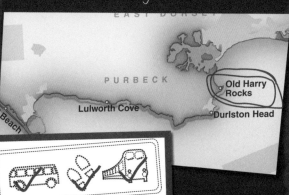

EAST DORSET

PURBECK

Old Harry Rocks

Lulworth Cove

Durlston Head

Beach

To Studland   To Wareham

PANEL LOCATION!
At the start of the footpath, outside the National Trust toilets, Studland.

GR: SZ 038825

Question:
About 35 million years ago the rocks were folded and faulted during uplift as A_____ collided with E_____ to form the A_____. Fill in the gaps.

25

To enter,

answer at least 6 questions, fill in your details and remember to complete the tie-breaker. Then detach this card, lick and stick it, and post it back to us.

Competition Rules

1. **Entry:** You can enter by completing the entry card opposite and posting it back to us, or you can enter at www.jurassiccoast.com and click on 'Explorers Competition'.
   You must answer at least 6 questions correctly and complete the tie-breaker in no more than 20 words.

2. **Number of Entries Allowed:** One entry and prize allowed per household.

3. **Entry Address:** EXPLORE THE JURASSIC COAST COMPETITION, Dorset County Council, Environmental Services, Freepost D0190, Dorchester DT1 1BR.

4. **Competition entry dates:** 2005 competition runs from 1st May 2005 to 1st October 2005 and entries must be received no later than 1st October 2005. 2006 competition runs from 1st November 2005 to 31st October 2006 and entries must be received no later than 31st October 2006. 2007 competition runs from 1st November 2006 to 31st October 2007 and entries must be received no later than 31st October 2007.

5. **The Prize:** The prize for 2005 is a four night mini-break at PGL Osmington Bay, Nr Weymouth, for up to two adults and four children (under 18s). Accommodation is an en suite family room, which may have bunk beds. Activities are not suitable for children under 6. Full mini-break details will be supplied to the winner following notification. Dorset and Devon County Councils/PGL reserve the right to offer alternative accommodation if this centre becomes unavailable for any reason. Dates of the 2005 mini-break are as follows:
   Accommodation nights – 24th to 27th October 2005
   Check in time on day of arrival is between 1600-1800
   Check out time on day of departure is between 0900-1100
   There will be an Activity Break prize of similar quality and value on offer for 2006 and 2007.

6. **There is no cash alternative.**

7. **Entry Restrictions:** This competition is not open to employees of Dorset or Devon County Council, English Nature or PGL, their immediate families, agents or anyone professionally connected with the promotion. Entries by third parties or in bulk not accepted.

8. **Independence of Judging:** The competition will be judged by a panel of 3 people, 2 from the World Heritage Team and 1 independent member, and drawn in front of an independent Auditor.

9. **Winner Notification:** Winners will be chosen by the panel.
   Winner of 2005 competition will be notified in writing by 7th October 2005.
   Winner of 2006 competition will be notified in writing by 7th October 2006.
   Winner of 2007 competition will be notified in writing by 7th October 2007.

10. **Winner Details:** The winners' names, addresses and winning tie-breaker answers can be requested by sending an SAE to the address below after the notification dates shown above.

11. **Promoter's Name and Address:** World Heritage Team, Environmental Services, Dorset County Council, County Hall, Colliton Park, Dorchester, Dorset DT1 1XJ.

12. **Publicity:** Dorset and Devon County Councils reserves the right to feature names, photographs and towns of competition winners in future publicity and promotions.

13. **Dorset and Devon County Councils take no responsibility for lost, delayed or damaged entries. Illegible entries will not be accepted.**

14. **Data Protection:** Dorset and Devon County Councils will occasionally send you information and special offers about Jurassic Coast by post. If you do not wish to receive such information, please tick here. ☐
    The judges' decision is final and no correspondence will be entered into.

Competition questions and answers

1. Orcombe Point: What causes the striking red colour of the cliffs?

2. Budleigh Salterton: What does 'Salterton' mean and why is the town so called?

3. Jacob's Ladder: What did the Rhynchosaur eat?

4. Beer: What are coccoliths?

5. Lyme Regis: What is the name of the most active coastal landslide in Britain?

6. Charmouth: What is the scientific name for a sea lily? (It begins with 'C'!)

7. Chesil Beach and the Fleet Lagoon: About how many tonnes of pebbles make up Chesil Beach?

8. Portland Bill: What are the fractures called which criss-cross Portland Stone and help the quarry men work the stone?

9. Lulworth Cove and Stair Hole: How many types of rock can be found at Lulworth Cove?

10. Durlston: What does the term 'discordant coastline' mean?

11. Old Harry: About 35 million years ago the rocks were folded and faulted during uplift as A_____ collided with E_____ to form the A_____. Fill in the gaps.

Name _____ **Age** _____

Address _____

_____ **Postcode** _____

Tie-breaker Question: Tell us in no more than 20 words why... **I would like to come back to the Jurassic Coast because...** _____

Explore the Jurassic Coast

EXPLORE THE JURASSIC COAST COMPETITION
DORSET COUNTY COUNCIL
ENVIRONMENTAL SERVICES
FREEPOST D0190
DORCHESTER
DT1 1BR